Little Look and Find™

DISNEP PRESENTS A PIXAR FILM

THE INCREDIBLES

ILLUSTRATED BY ART MAWHINNEY
COVER INSET ILLUSTRATED BY THE DISNEY STORYBOOK ARTISTS

© DISNEY ENTERPRISES, INC./PIXAR
THE TERM OMNIDROID USED BY PERMISSION OF LUCASFILM LTD.

PUBLISHED BY
LOUIS WEBER, C.E.O., PUBLICATIONS INTERNATIONAL, LTD.
7373 NORTH CICERO AVENUE, LINCOLNWOOD, ILLINOIS 60712

GROUND FLOOR, 59 GLOUCESTER PLACE, LONDON W1U 8JJ

CUSTOMER SERVICE: 1-800-595-8484 OR
CUSTOMER_SERVICE@PILBOOKS.COM

WWW.PILBOOKS.COM

8 7 6 5 4 3 2 1

ISBN-13: 978-1-4127-6517-6
ISBN-10: 1-4127-6517-X

P I KIDS IS A REGISTERED TRADEMARK OF
PUBLICATIONS INTERNATIONAL, LTD.
LOOK AND FIND IS A REGISTERED TRADEMARK OF
PUBLICATIONS INTERNATIONAL, LTD.
LITTLE LOOK AND FIND IS A TRADEMARK OF
PUBLICATIONS INTERNATIONAL, LTD.

publications international, ltd.
pi kids®

IN THE GOLDEN AGE OF HEROES, THERE WAS PLENTY OF SAVING TO DO TO KEEP THE SUPERS BUSY. LOOK FOR THESE SUPERS AS THEY PROTECT MUNICIBERG FROM VILLAINOUS PLOTS AND MISFORTUNATE ACCIDENTS.

ELASTIGIRL

MR. INCREDIBLE

FROZONE

THUNDERHEAD

GAZERBEAM

DYNAGUY

STRATOGALE

EVERY DAY CAN BE A CHALLENGE FOR SUPERS WHO ARE LIVING UNDERCOVER. IT'S DINNER WITH THE PARRS. THE DOORBELL IS RINGING, JACK-JACK IS MAKING A MESS, AND THE FOOD IS GETTING COLD. LOOK THROUGH THE DINING ROOM AND FIND THESE LEFTOVERS THAT THE PARRS ARE EATING.

LAST NIGHT'S MEATLOAF

FROZEN DE-LITE

SUNDAY PEPPERS

MEXI-CORN CARNE

BUSY-DAY CASSEROLE

CHEEZY ROLL-UP

CHERRIES JUBILEE

MR. INCREDIBLE HAS ARRIVED AT THE REMOTE ISLAND OF NOMANISAN IN ORDER TO BATTLE SYNDROME'S LEARNING ROBOT, THE OMNIDROID. FIND THESE OTHER NIFTY INVENTIONS AND GADGETS WHILE MR. INCREDIBLE TAKES CARE OF THIS HI-TECH ROBOT.

YOU'VE JUST ARRIVED AT EDNA MODE'S SUPER-CLASSIFIED, TOP-SECRET LABORATORY. SHE'S BUSY AT WORK, COMING UP WITH ALL KINDS OF NEW FABRICS AND THREADS TO BUILD SUPER SUITS THAT ARE INDESTRUCTIBLE AND FASHIONABLE. TRY TO FIND THESE DESIGNS OF NEW SUPER SUITS.

A MASK

A HOMING DEVICE

BOOTS

BODY SUIT

GLOVES

ELASTIGIRL'S SUIT

BELT

IT'S BACK TO THE ISLAND OF NOMANISAN FOR EVEN MORE HEART-POUNDING ACTION! THE INCREDIBLES HAVE THEIR HANDS FULL, BATTLING SYNDROME AND HIS TEAM OF GUARDS. NOW TAKE A QUICK BREAK FROM THE COMBAT TO SEARCH THE VOLCANIC ISLAND FOR THESE TROPICAL FRUITS.

A COMELY KUMQUAT

A MAGNIFICENT MANGO

A BEAUTIFUL BANANA

A PALATABLE PAPAYA

A PASSIONATE PASSION FRUIT

A GORGEOUS GUAVA

A FUZZY KIWI

IT HAS ALL COME DOWN TO ONE LAST BATTLE IN WHICH THE INCREDIBLES MUST DEFEAT SYNDROME'S ROBOT THAT IS OUT OF CONTROL IN THE CITY OF METROVILLE. THE GRATEFUL PUBLIC CHEERS THE RETURN OF THE SUPERS. TRY TO SPOT THESE PEOPLE WHO ARE MIXED INTO THE CROWD.

MRS. HOGENSON

DON RICHARDS

WENDY DAY

FIREFIGHTER LOPEZ

MAYOR ANDREWS

OFFICER O'LEARY

SNUG PORTER

RUSTY

JOHN BURROWS

FINALLY, A HAPPY ENDING! THE PARRS ARE BACK TO THEIR NORMAL LIVES, AS NORMAL AS CAN BE FOR AN UNDERCOVER SUPER FAMILY. DASH MAKES SURE TO COME IN A CLOSE SECOND AT THE SCHOOL TRACK MEET. SEARCH THE TRACK AND BLEACHERS TO FIND SOME OF DASH'S CLASSMATES.

HEAD BACK TO THE GOLDEN AGE OF HEROES TO FIND THESE ACTION VEHICLES:

- [ ] THE INCREDIBILE
- [ ] UPSIDE-DOWN POLICE CAR
- [ ] CITY AMBULANCE
- [ ] FIRE ENGINE
- [ ] STRETCH LIMO
- [ ] INVISIBLE JET

RE-ENTER INSURICARE AND FIND THESE BUSY OFFICE WORKERS:

- [ ] WINDOW WASHER
- [ ] COMPUTER GEEK
- [ ] JANITOR
- [ ] TYPEWRITER REPAIR PERSON
- [ ] WATER COOLER MAINTENANCE PERSON
- [ ] MAIL DELIVERY PERSON
- [ ] SECURITY OFFICER
- [ ] COPY CLERK

ZAM!

RETURN TO THE PARR DINING ROOM IN ORDER TO FIND ALL OF THESE FAMILY KEEPSAKES:

- [ ] HEIRLOOM POCKET WATCH
- [ ] DASH'S BRONZED BABY SHOES
- [ ] PHOTO OF THEIR HAWAIIAN VACATION
- [ ] SOUVENIR PLATE FROM THE CAPITAL
- [ ] VIOLET'S SILVER BABY CUP
- [ ] HELEN AND BOB'S WEDDING PORTRAIT
- [ ] MATCHING WEDDING GOBLETS

FLY BACK TO THE ISLAND OF NOMANISAN TO FIND EVEN MORE GADGETS:

SNEAK BACK INTO E'S LAB TO FIND THESE HI-TECH TOOLS:

- [ ] SONIC SCISSORS
- [ ] TAPE RECORDER
- [ ] TEK-LON PATTERN PROJECTOR
- [ ] MICRO SEWING MACHINE
- [ ] TEST PILOT IV
- [ ] VACUUMFORM

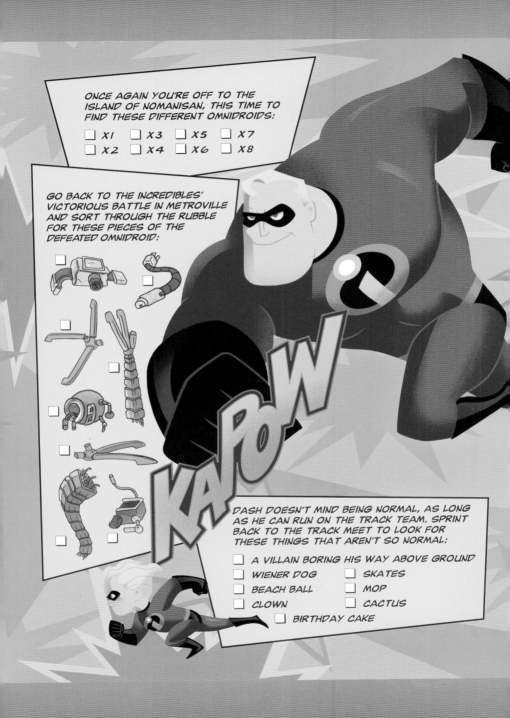

ONCE AGAIN YOU'RE OFF TO THE
ISLAND OF NOMANISAN, THIS TIME TO
FIND THESE DIFFERENT OMNIDROIDS:

☐ X1 ☐ X3 ☐ X5 ☐ X7
☐ X2 ☐ X4 ☐ X6 ☐ X8

GO BACK TO THE INCREDIBLES'
VICTORIOUS BATTLE IN METROVILLE
AND SORT THROUGH THE RUBBLE
FOR THESE PIECES OF THE
DEFEATED OMNIDROID:

KAPOW
KAPOW

DASH DOESN'T MIND BEING NORMAL, AS LONG
AS HE CAN RUN ON THE TRACK TEAM. SPRINT
BACK TO THE TRACK MEET TO LOOK FOR
THESE THINGS THAT AREN'T SO NORMAL:

☐ A VILLAIN BORING HIS WAY ABOVE GROUND
☐ WIENER DOG   ☐ SKATES
☐ BEACH BALL   ☐ MOP
☐ CLOWN   ☐ CACTUS
       ☐ BIRTHDAY CAKE